Humph...
of Fur...

Praise for *The World According to Humphrey*:

'A charming, feel-good tale.' *Irish Times*

'A breezy, well-crafted first novel. Humphrey's matter-of-fact, table-level view of the world is alternately silly and profound and Birney captures his unique blend of innocence and earnestness from the start.' *Publisher's Weekly*

Praise for *Friendship According to Humphrey*:

'An effective exploration of the joys and pains of making and keeping friends, which will strike a chord with many children.' *Daily Telegraph*

Praise for *Trouble According to Humphrey*:

'Children fall for Humphrey, and you can't beat him for feelgood life lessons.' *Sunday Times*

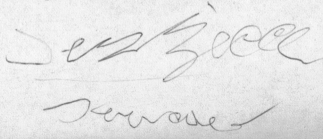

Humphrey's Book of Fun-Fun-Fun

Betty G. Birney worked at Disneyland and the Disney Studios, has written numerous children's television shows and is the author of over thirty-five books, including the bestselling *The World According to Humphrey*, which won the Richard and Judy Children's Book Club, *Friendship According to Humphrey*, *Trouble According to Humphrey*, *Surprises According to Humphrey*, *More Adventures According to Humphrey* and *Holidays According to Humphrey*. Her work has won many awards, including an Emmy and three Humanitas Prizes. She lives in America with her husband.

By Betty G. Birney

The World According to Humphrey
Friendship According to Humphrey
Trouble According to Humphrey
Adventure According to Humphrey
(special publication for World Book Day 2008)
Surprises According to Humphrey
More Adventures According to Humphrey
Holidays According to Humphrey
Humphrey's Big-Big-Big Book of Stories

The Princess and the Peabodys

Humphrey's Book of Fun-Fun-Fun

Betty G. Birney

Compiled by Amanda Li

ff

faber and faber

First published in 2010
by Faber and Faber Limited
Bloomsbury House, 74-77 Great Russell Street
London WC1B 3DA

Printed in England by CPI Bookmarque, Croydon

Graphic design by Ali Walper

A CIP record for this book
is available from the British Library

978–0–571–25424–8

2 4 6 8 10 9 7 5 3

What's in a Name?

My friends in Room 26 of Longfellow School all have very different personalities. Some are quiet, some are noisy, and one of them is **VERY-VERY-VERY** giggly! Our teacher, Mrs Brisbane, has special names for her students. Can you remember them? Find the missing words in the column on the right and write them in the correct space to complete my friends' names.

1. _Speak_-Up-Sayeh

2. Raise-your-_hand_Heidi

3. Pay-_Attention_Art

4. Lower-Your-_voice_ A.J.

5. Stop-_Giggling_Gail

6. _Repeat_-it-Please-Richie

7. Sit-_Still_ Seth

8. Wait-for-the-_bell_

Garth

7 STILL
3 ATTENTION
5 GIGGLING
6 REPEAT
1 SPEAK
2 HAND
8 BELL
4 VOICE

Humphrey's Favourite ♡ Things

There are so many things in life that are **GOOD-GOOD-GOOD**! Can you guess what some of my favourite things are? If you get the correct answers going across the word grid, you will find another special thing that belongs to me in the vertical box.

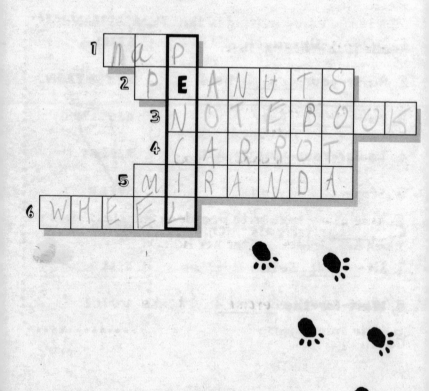

1. I'm a nocturnal creature so there's nothing I like more than to take a little _____ during the day.

2. Mmm! I just love to nibble up these tasty, salty snacks! Humans like them too — but sadly some have an allergy to them.

3. I really enjoy writing in this. Then, afterwards, I hide it somewhere safe.

4. Oh yes! Another yummy snack for me! This one is orange, crunchy and very good for you.

mmm!

5. One of my favourite people in the class. I call her 'Golden', after her hair.

6. When I need exercise, I just take a little spin in this.

Describe Humphrey

I don't like to show off, but humans do sometimes say that I'm quite a handsome little fellow! Can you find and circle six other words that describe me? That will leave six words that really don't fit me at all!

FURRY   SLIMY   LARGE

CLEVER

FRIENDLY

SCALY

BORING

SMALL

CUTE

HELPFUL   HEAVY   UNKIND

Now finish the following sentence using the circled words:

I think Humphrey is _____

_____

Tasty Treats Wordsearch

Mmm, I have so many favourite foods that I love to snack on! My pal Aldo knows exactly what I like and always brings me a tasty little something. Yum! Can you find eight tasty hamster treats in this yummy, scrummy wordsearch? They might be up, down, across or diagonal.

APPLE • PEAR • CARROT • NUTS
SEEDS • CHEESE • RAISINS • BROCCOLI

S	E	L	P	P	A	C	P	B
T	R	A	U	A	H	U	N	R
E	O	S	E	E	D	S	T	A
E	C	B	E	F	C	E	P	I
A	P	S	L	B	A	C	K	S
S	E	G	I	R	R	E	U	I
T	A	U	H	A	R	I	E	N
B	R	O	C	C	O	L	I	S
C	E	M	A	S	T	U	N	W

Mixed-Up Pets

Pet-O-Rama is the shop where lovely Ms Mac first found me. (Of course, my home is now in Longfellow School.) But all the pets I left behind have got their names mixed up – can you help to unscramble them?

1. t a c   _ _ _

2. o d g   _ _ _

3. e s u m o   _ _ _ _ _

4. r e b l i g   _ _ _ _ _ _

5. u n e g a i g i p   _ _ _ _ _ _   _ _ _

6. s h e r m a t   _ _ _ _ _ _ _

Rodent Rampage

Uh-oh! All these rodent pets – hamsters, gerbils, mice and guinea pigs – have escaped from the pet shop! Can you get them back to Pet-O-Rama before Carl the assistant discovers they're gone?

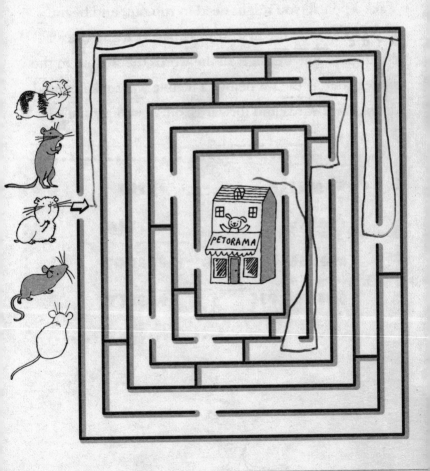

Pet Shop Wordsnake

Thank goodness there weren't any snakes at Pet-O-Rama, but here's a very different kind of snake – a wordsnake. (Believe me, this kind is much easier to deal with!)

Take a pencil (you might need to rub out) and begin at **START**. Find the first word **HAMSTER** and trace a continuous line through all the words that follow, in the same order as the list below. The line will snake up and down, backwards and forwards, but *never* diagonally.

HAMSTER	PUPPY
GERBIL	KITTEN
MOUSE	PARROT
GUINEA PIG	RABBIT

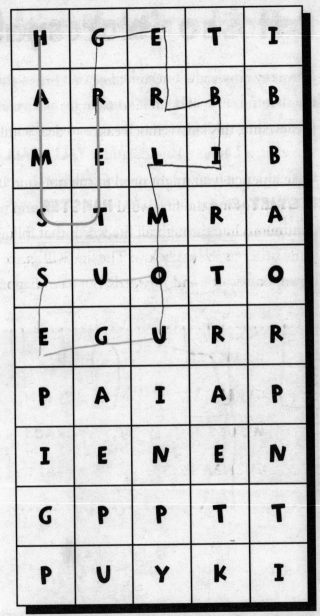

H	G	E	T	I
A	R	R	B	B
M	E	L	I	B
S	T	M	R	A
S	U	O	T	O
E	G	U	R	R
P	A	I	A	P
I	E	N	E	N
G	P	P	T	T
P	U	Y	K	I

A House for Humphrey

I love my cosy cage, but sometimes it's fun to think about my dream house and what it might be like. At Pet-O-Rama, they sold some very fancy hamster homes – there was even a Chinese Pagoda and a **TALL-TALL-TALL** castle! Can you get creative and design a wonderful hamster house for me?

Name the Pet

I think the name 'Humphrey' has a very nice ring to it, and it's the perfect name for a hamster since both words begin with 'H'!

Can you give each of these pets a name that begins with the same letter as the animal, like 'George gerbil'?

1. _Cathy_ **cat**

2. _Davie_ **dog**

3. _Ramona_ **rabbit**

4. _Milly_ **mouse**

5. _Fleur_ **fish**

6. _Phillip_ **parrot**

Humphrey's Hamster Challenge

Get your pencils ready – this challenge will get your brain spinning as fast as my wheel! How many words can you make using only the letters in the word below?

H A M S T E R

Write your words below. I've done one to start you off.

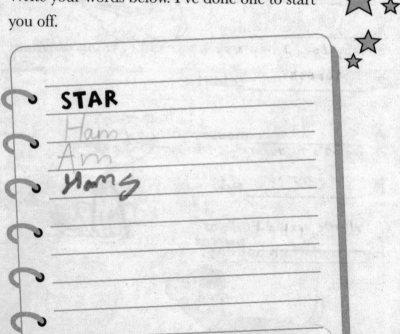

STAR

Ham

Am

Hams

Humphrey's Jokes 1

You probably know by now that I'm a hamster with a great sense of humour! I love to hear my friends telling each other jokes, and I write down the funniest ones in my notebook. Here are some of my most favourite jokes – about me!

1. Why does Humphrey love running round his wheel so much?

Because it's WHEELY-WHEELY-WHEELY fun!

2. Why does Humphrey write everything down in his notebook?

Because he can be a bit fur-getful.

3. What's Humphrey's favourite game?

Hide and Squeak!

4. Where would Humphrey love to visit on holiday?

Hamsterdam.

Mrs Brisbane's Spelling Test

I do love to take Mrs Brisbane's weekly spelling tests! I write all my answers in my little notebooks, and, even though I'm not as good a speller as Speak-Up-Sayeh, I usually get most of them right! Test your spelling skills in one of Mrs Brisbane's tests. Just (circle) the correct word in each pair. **WARNING**: they get harder as they go along!

1. write/rite
2. lite/light
3. little/litle
4. scool/school

5. woud/would
6. beak/beek
7. different/diffrent
8. becaws/because
9. beleive/believe
10. Wednesday/Wendsday

Aldo's Antics Dot-to-Dot

My good friend Aldo the caretaker loves to talk to me while he cleans Room 26, and he also does amazing tricks. Do you know what he is balancing on his fingertip? Join the dots to find out!

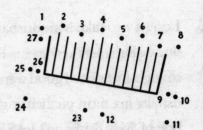

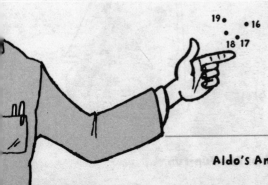

Humphrey's Rhyme Time

Help! Our class is studying poetry with Mrs Brisbane this week, and I've been writing my own little verses in my notebook. But I've left out one word in each of my poems. Can you fill in the missing rhyming word, **PLEASE-PLEASE-PLEASE**?

1. You know, I think it's really cool,
To be a student at Longfellow _____.

2. Aldo the caretaker cleans up our room,
He uses a mop,
a bucket and _____.

3. One time, I had a
lovely float,
On Potter's Pond,
aboard a _____.

4. I had an adventure and rode a fast train,
But I'm really not keen to do it _____.

5. Og is my fellow classroom pet,
He lives in a tank and likes to get _____.

6. I have many good friends, including Og,
But I'm not a big fan of Miranda's pet _____.

(Hey, can you remember the name of Miranda's big hairy pet?) Clem

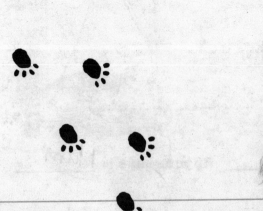

My Favourite ♡ Pet

I **LOVE-LOVE-LOVE** being a pet! It's so great to be looked after and cared for by a human friend – and so interesting to find out about their lives, especially since they behave in very peculiar ways!

If you could have any pet in the world, what would it be? (Maybe a hamster? They make very rewarding pets, you know.) Draw your imaginary pet below and give it a name.

My pet is a ___Hamster___   My pet's name is ___Humphery___

Sleepy Wordsearch

Oh I do love my naps! And my little sleeping area is so cosy and warm to snuggle up in after a hard night's spinning on my wheel! This very sleepy wordsearch contains eight sleep-related words. Can you find them? They might be up, down, across or diagonal.

SLEEP • BED • SNORE • YAWN
DOZE • NAP • PILLOW • DREAM

O	W	A	E	R	Y	A	D
P	I	L	L	O	W	B	N
A	S	Y	D	O	Z	E	R
N	O	B	R	P	A	I	S
E	W	Z	E	D	N	E	N
P	L	E	A	P	E	R	O
E	L	I	M	L	O	B	R
S	U	Y	A	W	N	A	E

True or False?

I've learned a lot about humans and their behaviour by visiting the homes of my friends in Room 26. And they've learned a lot about me and how I live. In fact, I'd say they have all become hamster experts! How much do you think you know about hamsters? Find out by reading the ten sentences below and deciding if they are true or false.

1. **Hamsters are usually very good at escaping from their cages.**
   TRUE ☑   FALSE ☐

2. **Hamsters sometimes store food in their ears.**
   TRUE ☐   FALSE ☑

3. **When hamsters feel scared or threatened, they sometimes puff up their cheeks.**
   TRUE ☑   FALSE ☐

4. Hamsters are not very good at climbing.

TRUE ☐   FALSE ☑

5. Hamsters have long tails.

TRUE ☐   FALSE ☑

6. Other animals such as cats and dogs could harm a hamster.

TRUE ☑   FALSE ☐

7. The dwarf hamster is the smallest type of hamster.

TRUE ☑   FALSE ☐

8. In the wild, hamsters usually live in trees.

TRUE ☐   FALSE ☑

9. Hamsters are able to carry up to half their body weight in their cheek pouches.

TRUE ☑   FALSE ☐

10. The hamster gets its name from a German word for storing food: 'hamstern'.

TRUE ☑   FALSE ☐

Humphrey's Halloween Match-Up

I thought Halloween (or is it Howloween?) would be
scary at first but then I realised it was **FUN-FUN-FUN!**
Playing Trick-or-Squeak, dressing up in costumes . . .
We even put on a great show!

Afterwards, all the Halloween things were left in Room 26. There are two of everything. Can you match up the pairs by drawing lines? When you've finished, you will find one thing left over that has nothing to do with Halloween. What is it?

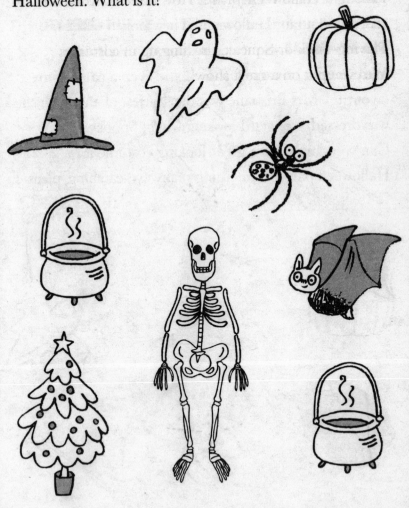

Humphrey's Halloween Costume

I hardly recognised my classmates when they were all dressed up for Halloween! They looked **GREAT-GREAT-GREAT** as pirates, a dragon, a skeleton, a mad scientist, an angel, a devil and even a cat (not my favourite). Mrs Brisbane was the scariest of them all: she was dressed as a weird-looking witch! Spooky!

Can you design me a great-looking costume for a Halloween party? Something really eye-catching, please!

Mad (everything)

Pumpkin Pairs

Halloween is a whole lot of fun, especially when everyone dresses up in costumes and goes trick-or-treating. But I try not to look at the pumpkin lanterns – I find them a little scary! Can you match up these five pairs of pumpkins by drawing lines between them? I can't do it – I'm covering my eyes with my paws!

Humphrey's Jokes 2

Get ready for some more of my favourite hamster jokes – they really are unsqueakably funny!

Q. What did the mummy hamster say to her kids at bedtime?
A. 'I'm sorry kids, I don't have a tale.'

Q. Why do hamsters need oiling?
A. Because they squeak!

Ha ha!

Q. What do you call a hamster that can pick up an elephant?
A. Sir!

Q. What do hamsters do when they're not running on their wheels?
A. Mousework.

Help Humphrey

I **LOVE-LOVE-LOVE** mazes, don't you? Garth and A.J. have built me a terrific maze, filled with confusing twists and turns. But it's a little too tricky – even for an especially clever hamster like me! Can you help me find my way out?

WAY OUT

Puzzling Pals

School's over for today, and I've just come out of my cage to visit my tank-dwelling pal, Og the Frog. Don't we make a handsome pair of classroom pets?

Look carefully at our two pictures, and see
if you can find six differences between them.

Pet Picture Puzzler

Mmm, tricky! All these pet names fit into the grid opposite, but where do they go? Look at the pictures and write the words in the correct spaces. I've written in one (very important) letter to help you.

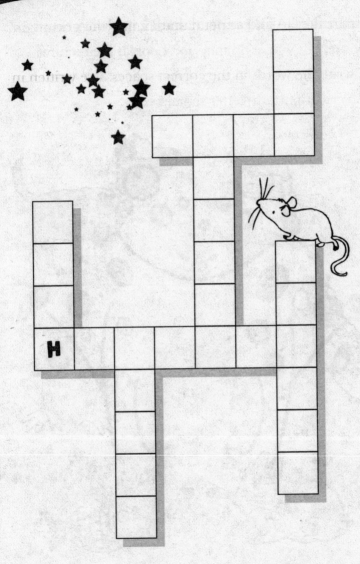

H

My Dot-to-Dot Pal

Join the dots to find a friend that I can always count on.

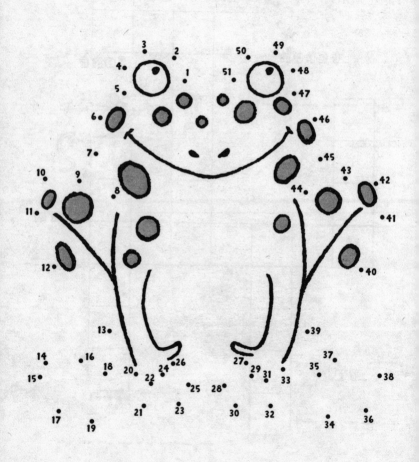

Mixed-Up Humphrey

Eek! All these words for parts of my body have got mixed up. Can you unscramble them and write the words in the spaces? Then draw a line matching the right word to the right part of my body.

eckeh

_ _ _ _ _ _

sone

_ _ _ _

yee

eye

era

ear

walc

_ _ _ _

skiwresh

_ _ _ _ _ _ _ _

Humphrey's Jokes 3

Enough of all the hamster jokes – what about my fellow rodents? I think they deserve a laugh or two, don't you? Get ready to giggle at my very favourite mouse jokes!

Q. What does a mouse put in his drink?
A. Mice cubes!

Q. What has twelve legs, six eyes, three tails and can't see a thing?
A. Three blind mice.

Q. What are small, furry and brilliant at sword fights?
A. The Three Mouseketeers!

Q. What do angry rodents send each other at Christmas?
A. Cross mouse cards!

Q. How do mice celebrate when they move house?
A. They have a mouse-warming party.

Miranda's Memory Challenge

I had a wonderful time exploring Golden Miranda's desktop when I stayed at her house. (Oh, happy memories – except for her fur-raising dog, Clem!) And I can remember everything I sniffed. Let's see if your memory is as good as mine. Take a good look at Miranda's desk for one minute. Then close the book, or cover up the picture. Can you remember seven things that are on Miranda's desk?

More of Humphrey's Rhymes

Making up poems about myself is really **FUN-FUN-FUN**! I've written six more rhymes in my notebook and left out one word each time. Can you fill in the missing rhyming word?

1. **Nuts and carrots, what a treat, To have delicious things to** _eat_ .

2. **I can't describe how good I feel, When I am spinning on my** _wheel_ .

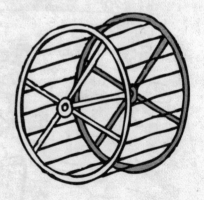

3. Being nocturnal is how I'll stay,
I wake at night, I doze all ___day___.

4. Being a hamster, I like to squeak
And keep my food inside my ___cheak___.

5. I hide my notebook out of sight,
So nobody knows I can read and ___write___.

6. I don't much like being prodded or poked,
But I **LOVE-LOVE-LOVE**
being petted and ___stoked___.

Aldo's Word Ladder 1

I like watching Aldo as he does useful jobs around the school. But today he's got a tricky puzzle for you to solve! Read the first clue and change one letter in the word **RAT** to get the answer. Continue down the ladder in the same way but remember you can only change **ONE LETTER** each time. If you do it right, you'll end up with the same word that you started with.

1. Hamsters like it if you give them a gentle stroke or _____.

2. Hamsters are a very popular _____.

3. The opposite of dry is _____.

4. You can catch fish with a _____.

5. I like to eat a crunchy pea_____.

6. A little house is sometimes called a _____.

7. The opposite of cold is _____.

8. Something you wear on your head is a _____.

9. Change one letter and you'll get back to **RAT**.

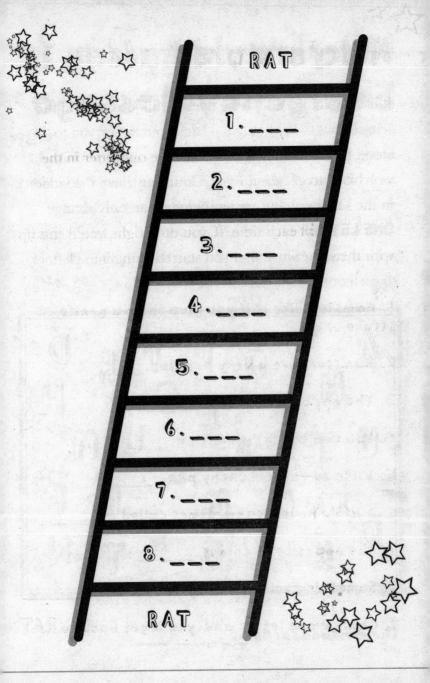

RAT

1. ___
2. ___
3. ___
4. ___
5. ___
6. ___
7. ___
8. ___

RAT

Humphrey's Emergency Message

Once, when Aldo disappeared and a complete stranger took his place, I admit I got a little panicked. I decided to use Mrs Brisbane's practice letters to spell out a message. Can you read it? Cross out all the letters that appear twice. Then jiggle around the remaining letters to spell out the message in the space below.

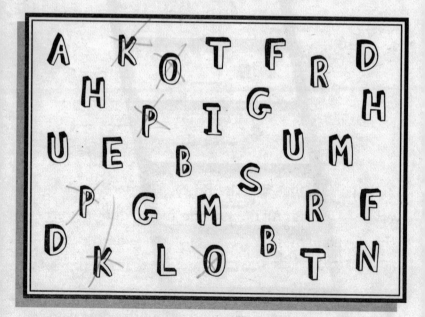

The message spells _ _ _ _ _ _ _ !

The Wrong Hand Art Contest

Left hand Right

* **My Wrong Hand drawing is a** _Hamster_ *

On Wacky Wednesday Mrs Brisbane had a fun (and very wacky) idea. All the students had to draw pictures with the hand they didn't usually draw with. It ended up in a Wrong Hand Art Contest – and all the drawings looked pretty strange! Why don't you have a try? Draw something you are usually good at, but this time with the wrong hand. How does it look?

Humphrey's Secret Code

Shhh!

A ☀   J ✏   S

B 🌙   K 🖌   T

C ⭐   L 🍎   U

D 🍃   M 🍌   V

E 🌸   N 🍪   W

F ♡   O   X 🔒

G 🦋   P   Y

H 🌈   Q   Z

I 📖   R 🎸

I'm very good at keeping secrets – and I love secret codes. They're **FUN-FUN-FUN** to solve! In my notebook I've been making up my own secret code using pictures of things that I like. And now I've written *you* a message. It's a saying I heard in a great book Mrs Brisbane read to us by a famous writer called Robert Louis Stevenson. I think it's very true. Can you figure out what it is? Write each letter in the space as you find it.

In a Spin

As I spin on my wheel in Room 26, I can see Humphreyville, the incredible model town that my friends helped to build. Can you help too by matching up pairs of words that make different places in Humphreyville? Draw matching lines from one side of my wheel to the other.

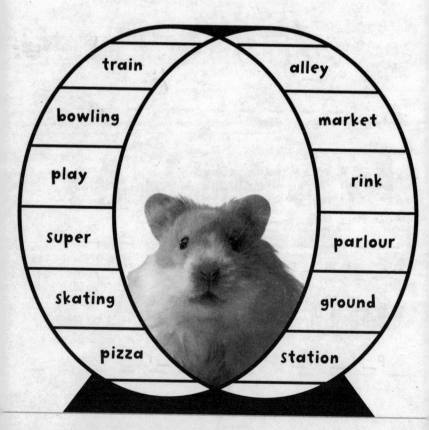

train   alley

bowling   market

play   rink

super   parlour

skating   ground

pizza   station

Finish the Job

When the class was building Humphreyville, our very own town, Mrs Brisbane asked us to think about all the different and important jobs that people did in real towns. Here's the list of jobs we made. Can you guess what they are? Fill in the vowels – that's a, e, i, o and u – to complete the jobs.

1. T _ _ c h _ r

2. D _ c t _ r

3. N _ r s _

4. D _ n t _ s t

5. S h _ p k _ _ p _ r

6. F _ r m _ r

7. B _ _ l d _ r

8. P _ l _ c _   _ f f _ c _ r

School Wordsnake

I've really gotten to know the students in Room 26 well during my time at Longfellow School. I can even spell all their names! Can you find their names in this winding wordsnake?

Use a pencil to draw a continuous line through the names in the grid (in the same order as the list below). The line will snake up and down, backwards and forwards, but *never* diagonally.

SAYEH	SETH
HEIDI	GARTH
ART	MANDY
GAIL	PAUL
RICHIE	A.J.
MIRANDA	

S	A	Y	J	A
H	H	E	U	L
E	R	T	A	P
I	A	G	D	Y
D	I	A	N	A
R	L	I	H	M
I	I	E	T	R
C	H	M	G	A
A	R	I	H	T
N	D	A	S	E

Humphrey's Odd One Out

Hmm… all these creatures in Pet-O-Rama may look the same, but if you look closely you'll spot a few differences. Can you circle one picture in each set of three that is the odd one out?

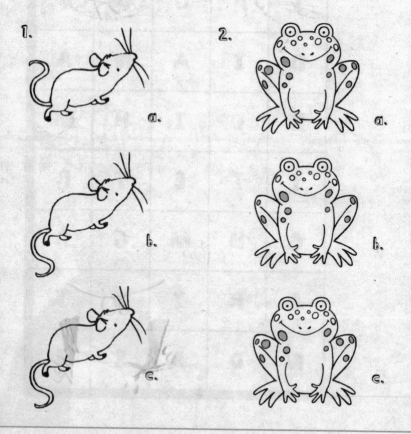

1.
a.
b.
c.

2.
a.
b.
c.

4.

a.

b.

c.

a.

b.

c.

Humphrey's Odd One Out   49

Og Dreams

My friend Og is a frog who doesn't say much, and sometimes I wonder what he's thinking about as he sits on a rock in his glass tank. What do you think Og daydreams about? Draw your idea in the thought bubble above Og's head.

Humphrey's Jokes 4

Og the frog doesn't say much – but when I tell him one of my Og jokes I always hear a loud and happy **BOING** coming from his tank! Here are some of his favourite frog funnies.

1. Why is Og so happy?

Because he can eat whatever bugs him!

2. How deep can Og go in water?

Knee-deep! Knee-deep!

3. What is Og's favourite drink?

Croaka-Cola!

4. Why did Og say 'Meow'?

He was learning a foreign language.

5. What kind of shoes does Og prefer?

Open toad.

True or False Frog Facts

Before I met Og, my knowledge of frogs was nothing to squeak of. But since we've been sharing Room 26, I've been finding out a lot more about these amazing amphibians and how they live. How much do you know? Test yourself by reading the ten sentences below and ticking the true or false box. Just take a guess if you don't know the answer!

Boing!

1. Some frogs live in the ocean.
TRUE ☑   FALSE ☑

2. Frogs don't drink water — they absorb it through their skin.
TRUE ☑   FALSE ☐

3. A frog is a reptile.
TRUE ☐   FALSE ☑

4. Frogs eat insects such as flies, mosquitoes and crickets. TRUE ☑ FALSE ☐

5. A frog catches its food with its front legs.
TRUE ☐ FALSE ☑

6. Some frogs can jump up to twenty times their body length in one leap.
TRUE ☑ FALSE ☐

7. Frogs have terrible hearing.
TRUE ☐ FALSE ☑

8. A frog can change the colour of its skin to blend in with its surroundings.
TRUE ☑ FALSE ☐

9. Only a male frog can croak.
TRUE ☑ FALSE ☐

10. A group of frogs is called an 'army'.
TRUE ☑ FALSE ☐

Ergh! What's Og's Snack?

It's safe to say that Og and I don't have the same taste when it comes to food. While I'm nibbling on my tasty fruit and vegetables, Og is more interested in munching . . . well, you'll have to do the puzzle to find out! Read the clues and write the names of all my favourite snacks in the grid opposite. Then you will find the name of Og's snack in the vertical box. **ERGH!**

1. An orange vegetable — rabbits love it too!

2. This is an occasional treat — yellow in colour and much loved by mice and humans. You'll always find it on a pizza!

3. A delicious fruit that grows on trees and makes an excellent pie filling. Poor Snow White was poisoned by one.

4. Tasty little snacks which also grow on trees and come in many varieties, such as pistachio.

5. These small crunchy snacks are very healthy. If you put one in the ground and watered it, perhaps a plant would grow from it one day.

1 C A R
R
I
K

2

3

4

5

yuck!

Dot-to-Dot Pet

Can you guess which creature this is? I'll give you a clue:
it's not a hamster, but it is one of my fellow rodents –
and we both like to squeak!

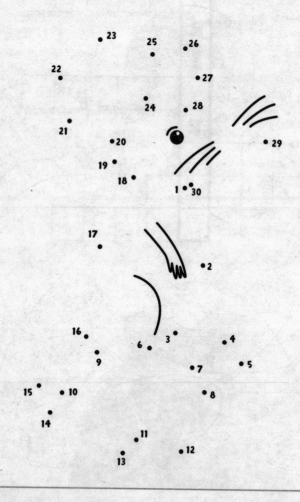

Trail of Treats

Oh, I'm hungry and I can't wait to get my teeth into a **YUMMY-YUMMY-YUMMY** snack! But only one trail leads to the apple. Can you choose the right one?

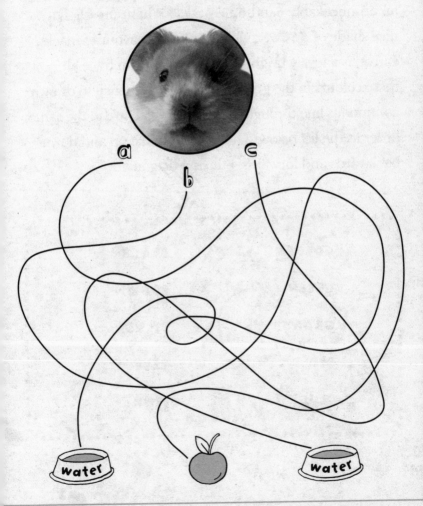

Humphrey's Colour Wordsnake

Colour is very important in my life. As you know, I am an unsqueakably handsome **golden** hamster. Og is a nice shade of **green**, while one of my favourite snacks, carrot, is a lovely bright **orange**. Can you trace all these colours in the grid opposite? Use a pencil to draw a continuous line through the words, which are in the same order as the list below. The line will snake up and down, backwards and forwards, but *never* diagonally.

GOLDEN	BLACK
GREEN	BROWN
ORANGE	SILVER
RED	YELLOW
BLUE	PINK

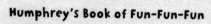

START ⟹

G	O	L	D	E
O	N	R	G	N
R	E	E	K	N
A	E	D	P	I
N	R	B	W	O
G	E	L	L	L
B	E	U	E	Y
L	R	O	E	R
A	B	W	V	L
C	K	N	S	I

Humphrey's Jokes 5

BOING!! Og can never seem to get enough of my hilarious frog jokes. So here are some more!

1. What's Og's favourite year?

A leap year, of course!

2. What's green, green, green, green and green?

Og rolling down a hill.

3. Where does Og get his eyes tested?

At the hoptician!

4. How does Og like to travel?

By hoppercraft.

5. Where does Og leave his coat at school?

In the croakroom.

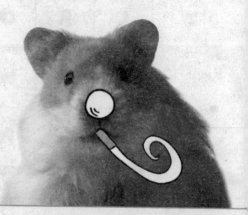

Complete Og

I enjoyed Richie's birthday party but I wasn't too impressed by Magic Mitch the magician. He had the nerve to make people's personal belongings completely disappear! Then (and this was very rude) he cut up Richie's banknote into lots of tiny pieces!

Now Magic Mitch has cut this picture of Og in half! Can you help by drawing the other half of the picture? *(Tip: it's a mirror image.)*

Humphrey's Haikus

I love living in Room 26 because Mrs Brisbane is always teaching us new and interesting things. At the moment we're looking at haikus, an ancient form of Japanese poetry. Some of them are just like tricky riddles! Try reading these animal haikus (I wrote them in the little notebook I keep hidden in my cage) and see if you can guess which creature I'm describing.

So big and hairy
Long tail and a loud, loud woof!
Please keep off my cage!

ANSWER _____

Happy in his tank
Hops and jumps on long green legs
Can you hear a 'Boing'?

ANSWER _____

Small, cute and furry
Watches humans from his cage
Spinning round his wheel

ANSWER _____

Would you like to write your own animal haiku?
First, think of a creature you'd like to write about.
Then read these simple haiku rules and get creative!

HAIKU RULES

1. A haiku is very short — it has only three lines.

2. The first and last lines have five syllables, and the middle line has seven syllables. You can count them on your fingers!

3. Haikus don't have to rhyme.

MY ANIMAL HAIKU

_____

_____

_____

Aldo's Word Ladder 2

Here comes Aldo with another tricky word puzzle for you to solve. And if you get the answers right you will magically change a **LOCK** into a **CAGE**! There are ten clues. Each answer is a four-letter word. Read the clue and change only **ONE LETTER** from the word before to get a new word.

1. Something you put on your foot before a shoe goes on. Sock

2. Another word for feeling unwell. Og's crickets sometimes make me feel like this! Bleurgh! Sick

3. The sound a clock makes. tojsck

4. I've noticed that some kids do this to their nose. Adults say it's a disgusting habit. Pick

5. What you have to do before you go on holiday. You need a suitcase for this. Pack

6. A great outdoor place where kids go to play and run around. Park

7. The opposite of light. It gets like this at nighttime. dark

8. Something sharp that is thrown in a game. It's smaller than an arrow. Dart

9. A sort of large container on wheels that you can push or pull around. It's great for holding lots of stuff. Cart

10. Your family and friends are the people who really CARE about you.

LOCK

1. S OCK
2. S ICK
3. T ICK
4. P ick
5. PACK
6. PARK
7. Dark
8. Dart
9. Cart
10. CARE

CAGE

Another Mysterious Message . . .

It was a very strange thing: one Friday morning, not a single person, not even Aldo, turned up at school. I couldn't work it out – then I looked out of the window! I used Mrs Brisbane's special letters to spell out the reason why. Cross out all the letters that appear twice, then rearrange the letters that are left over to find out why no one came to school that day.

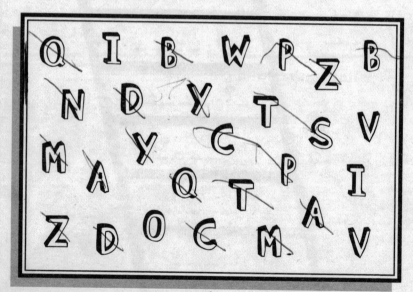

The reason why? _S_ _N_ _O_ _W_

Humphrey's Jokes 6

Specially selected for my great pal Og the frog (who has a great sense of humour but keeps it hidden), here's another hilarious page of froggy funnies. **BOING**

1. How would a frog feel if he broke his leg?

Unhoppy.

2. What's a frog's favourite music?

Hip-hop.

3. What do frogs order in restaurants?

French flies.

4. What's green and can jump a mile a minute?

A frog with hiccups.

5. Where do sick frogs go?

To the hopspital.

Boat Bonanza

YO-HO-HO! I once took an unsqueakably dangerous voyage on a tall ship across Potter's Pond. It was a thrilling adventure! Here are six pictures of me in full sail. Can you spot one picture that is slightly different to all the rest?

c

d

e

f

Boat Wordsearch

My friends in Room 26 worked very hard to build their brilliant boats, and we all learnt a lot about boats and ships at the same time. Here are eight different types of water vessel. Can you find them in the wordsearch below? They might be up, down, across or diagonal.

BOAT • SHIP • FERRY • JUNK • YACHT
CANOE • LONGBOAT • SUBMARINE

L	O	N	G	B	O	A	T	F	O
N	A	C	S	E	Y	G	P	E	T
E	J	U	N	K	A	J	N	R	A
R	C	B	Y	M	T	I	J	R	P
A	S	T	C	I	R	B	E	Y	T
K	N	A	H	A	H	O	R	Y	O
O	I	O	M	K	N	S	J	A	B
G	R	B	T	M	Y	O	G	C	I
Y	U	R	S	A	E	K	E	H	M
S	H	I	P	C	K	O	J	T	N

Design a Boat

Do you remember when the class built their own boats
and sailed them across Potter's Pond? And I almost got
a soaking – that was certainly a narrow squeak! The
boats were all sensational Miranda and Sayeh created
a graceful swan, A. J. and Garth made a sailing boat
with a skull and crossbones flag, while Art and Mandy
built a Viking ship. Wow! Could you design a boat too –
one that might win a prize for Most Beautiful or Most
Seaworthy Boat? Draw your idea below.

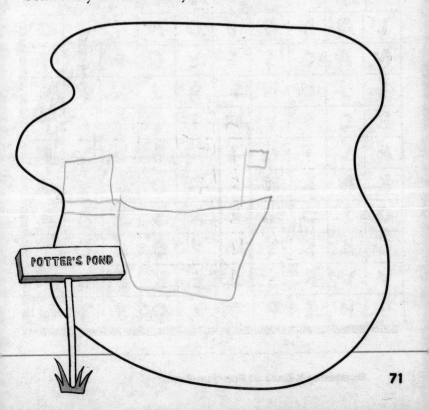

POTTER'S POND

Pirate Puzzle

Mrs Brisbane has been telling us some fur-raising stories about pirates! Now I know all about their thrilling adventures sailing the high seas.

How much do you know about pirates? Try this word puzzle and find out. If you get the five 'across' answers right, you will find a word that is something you might have to walk if you were unlucky enough to be captured by pirates . . . Good luck, me hearties!

1. A bird that squawks and sometimes sits on a pirate's shoulder.

2. Pirates can't wait to get their hands on this! It's inside the treasure chest, along with glittering jewels and silver.

3. All pirates need one of these to guide them to the buried treasure.

4. A place where the treasure is usually buried. Pirates must sail here as it is completely surrounded by sea.

5. You will find this scary-looking symbol on a pirate flag.

Aaaarrr!

☠ Pirate Wordsearch

Oh, I can never get enough of hearing Mrs Brisbane read us pirate stories! And I've learnt lots of new words from them (like 'Ahoy' and 'Avast'!) Can you find eight words that pirates use in the wordsearch below? They might be up, down, across or diagonal.

SAIL • SKULL • RUM • TREASURE
ISLAND • PARROT • HOOK • SHIP

T	O	R	R	A	P	L	E	U
I	M	U	T	O	L	R	N	P
U	H	M	O	I	U	R	M	S
P	A	D	H	S	H	O	O	K
N	I	T	A	L	S	K	I	U
D	K	E	O	A	S	A	I	L
S	R	O	L	N	M	U	T	L
T	H	R	U	D	P	N	I	R
P	I	H	S	I	K	K	A	H

Pirate Dot-to-Dot

Avast matey! Join the dots to discover a pirate's favourite pet.

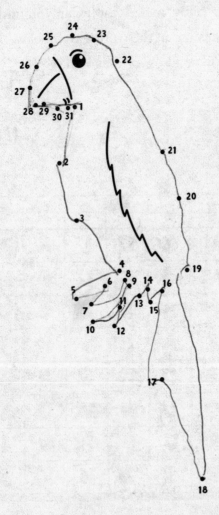

Humphrey's Pirate Secret Code

A ☀
B 🌙
C ⭐
D 🍃
E 🌸
F ♡
G 🦋
H 🌈
I 📖

J ✏
K 🖌
L 🍎
M 🍌
N 🍪
O 🥕
P ⛵
Q ⚾
R 🎻

S 🧹
T 🎁
U 🐸
V 🌳
W 🎡
X 🔒
Y 🧀
Z 🍐

Here's another of my **FUN-FUN-FUN** secret codes –
this time on a pirate theme. I got the idea from Mrs
Brisbane's thrilling book, *The Jolly Roger's Guide to Life*.
Can you work out what it is? I'll give you a clue: it's
something that pirates used to say. Write each letter in
the space as you find it.

A H O Y   T H E R E

M E   H E A R T I E S

Humphrey's Jokes 7

Argghh! I've been listening to the students telling each other some hilarious pirate jokes – here are my favourites. I hope they shiver ye timbers, landlubbers!

1. Where do you go to the bathroom on a pirate ship?

On the poop deck! Get it, poop deck! Herita

2. Why don't pirates know their alphabet properly?

Because they think there are seven 'c's.

3. What do you call a pirate who steals from the rich and gives to the poor?

Robin Hook.

4. How does a pirate with two hooks scratch his nose?

Very, very carefully!

5. Why don't pirates get hungry on desert islands?

Because of all the sand which is there.

Help Humphrey Get Home

As you probably know, my cage has a lock-that-doesn't-lock, so I can come and go as I please without anyone knowing. But now that I'm out, I can't find my way back! Can you help me get to my cage? And how many Nutri-Nibbles will I pick up along the way?

How Much Do You Know About Humphrey?

Have you read all the Humphrey books and think you know lots about me? Well, now's the time to see how much you can remember! Take a look at the questions below. Each has three possible answers – just tick the box to choose the correct one. If you're not sure, take a guess. Good luck!

1. What can Humphrey do that other hamsters (usually) can't?

☐ Fly a plane

☑ Read and write

☐ Play the piano

2. When Humphrey first gets to know Aldo, he's the school caretaker. Then Aldo decides to train for a new job. What does he want to be?

☑ A teacher

☐ A scientist

☐ A magician

3. Who is the headteacher of Longfellow School?

- [ ] Ms Mac
- [x] Mrs Brisbane
- [x] Mr Morales

4. What is Gail always doing in class?

- [ ] Grunting
- [x] Giggling
- [ ] Gossiping

5. For Halloween, what did Humphrey dress up as?

- [x] A ghost
- [ ] An alien
- [ ] A wizard

6. What pet does Golden Miranda own? (It's an animal that Humphrey really doesn't like.) ~~Clem~~ Clem

- [ ] A cat
- [ ] A snake
- [x] A dog

How Much Do You Know About Humphrey?

7. What is the number of the classroom that Humphrey lives in?

☑ 26

☐ 36

☐ 46

8. What kind of boat does Humphrey go sailing on during his Potter's Pond adventure?

☐ A pirate ship

☐ A Chinese junk

☑ A tall ship

9. Why does Miranda lose her job as the class animal keeper?

☐ She forgets to feed Humphrey.

☑ Humphrey gets out of his cage.

☐ She doesn't clean out his cage.

10. What noise does Og the frog usually make?

☑ Boing!
☑ Ribbit!
☐ Croak!

11. When Humphrey takes his first train ride, what does he almost crash into?

☐ A rollercoaster
☐ A train station
☑ A lake

12. What fun and special day does Mrs Brisbane think up for her class?

☐ Manic Monday
☑ Wacky Wednesday
☐ Fun-Fun-Fun Friday

Wow! You really know a lot about me. I'm impressed!

Answers

p. 1 **What's in a Name?** 1. Speak-Up-Sayeh 2. Raise-your-Hand-Heidi
3. Pay Attention-Art 4. Lower-Your-Voice A.J. 5. Stop-Giggling-Gail
6. Repeat-it-Please-Richie 7. Sit-Still-Seth 8. Wait-for-the-Bell-Garth

pp. 2–3 **Humphrey's Favourite Things**

```
1  N  A  P              Planet
2     P  E  A  N  U  T  S
3        N  O  T  E  B  O  O  K
4        C  A  R  R  O  T
5        M  I  R  A  N  D  A
6  W  H  E  E  L
```

p. 4 **Describe Humphrey.** The words that describe him are:
CUTE, FURRY, CLEVER, SMALL, FRIENDLY, HELPFUL

p. 5 **Tasty Treats Wordsearch**

```
S  E  L  P  P  A  C  P  B
T  R  A  U  A  H  U  N  R
E  O  S  E  E  D  S  T  A
E  C  B  E  F  C  E  P  I
A  P  S  L  B  A  C  K  S
S  E  G  I  R  R  E  U  I
T  A  U  H  A  R  I  E  N
B  R  O  C  C  O  L  I  S
C  E  M  A  S  T  U  N  W
```

p. 12 Mixed-Up Pets

1. Cat 2. Dog 3. Mouse
4. Gerbil 5. Guinea pig
6. Hamster

p. 13 Rodent Rampage

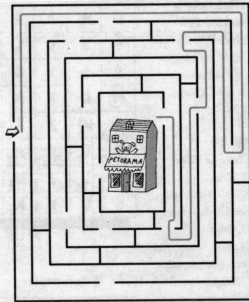

pp. 8–9 Pet Shop Wordsnake

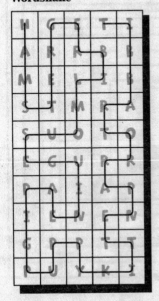

p. 12 Humphrey's Hamster Challenge

Here's all the words I found. Did you manage to find any others?

STREAM, EARTH, HEART, MARSH, MATHS, SHAME, SMART, STARE, STEAM, EAST, HARE, HEAR, HEAT, MAST, MATE, MEAT, REST, SAME, SEAT, STAR, STEM, TAME, TEAM, TEAR, TERM, TRAM, ARE, ARM, ART, ATE, EAR, EAT, HAM, HAT, HEM, HER, MAT, MET, RAM, RAT, SAT, SEA, SET, SHE, TEA, THE

p. 14 Mrs Brisbane's Spelling Test

1. write 2. light 3. little 4. school 5. would
6. beak 7. different 8. because 9. believe
10. Wednesday

pp. 16-17
Humphrey's Rhyme Time

School, broom, boat, again, wet, dog.
Miranda's pet dog is called Clem

pp. 20-21
True or False?

1. True
2. False – they store food in their cheeks.
3. True
4. False, hamsters are very good climbers.
5. False, hamsters have very short tails, sometimes you can't even see them!
6. True 7. True
8. False. In the wild, hamsters live in underground burrows.
9. True 10. True

pp. 22-23
Humphrey's Halloween Match-up

The item left over is a Christmas tree.

p. 19 Sleepy Wordsearch

O	W	A	E	R	Y	A	D
P	I	L	L	O	W	B	N
A	S	Y	D	O	Z	E	R
N	O	B	R	P	A	I	S
E	W	Z	E	D	N	E	N
P	L	E	A	P	E	R	O
E	L	I	M	L	O	B	R
S	U	Y	A	W	N	A	E

p. 27 Help Humphrey

pp. 30–31 Pet Picture Puzzler

p. 33 Mixed-up Humphrey

Clockwise: nose, ear, whiskers, claw, eye, cheek.

pp. 36–37 More of Humphrey's Rhymes

Eat, wheel, day, cheek, write, stroked.

pp. 38–39 Aldo's Word Ladder

RAT, PAT, PET, WET, NET, NUT, HUT, HOT, HAT, RAT.

p. 40 Humphrey's Emergency Message

Answer: **ALIENS**

pp. 42–43 Humphrey's Secret Code

Message reads: **A FRIEND IS A PRESENT YOU GIVE YOURSELF**

p. 44 In a Spin

Train station, bowling alley, playground, supermarket, skating rink, pizza parlour.

p. 45 Finish the Job

1. Teacher 2. Doctor 3. Nurse
4. Dentist 5. Shopkeeper 6. Farmer
7. Builder 8. Police Officer

pp. 46–47 School Wordsnake

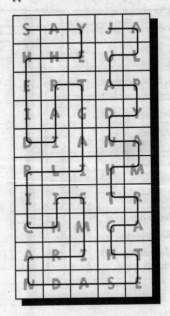

pp. 48–49 Humphrey's Odd One Out

Answers: 1A, 2B, 3C, 4B.

pp. 52–53 True or False Frog Facts.

Answers: 1. False
2. True 3. False, frogs are
amphibians
4. True 5. False – a frog
catches food with its long
sticky tongue.
6. True 7. False – frogs have
very good hearing.
8. True 9. True 10. True!

pp. 54–55 Urgh! What's Og's Snack?

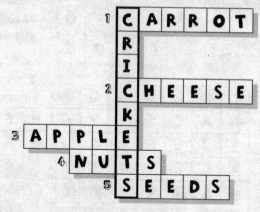

p. 57 Trail of Treats Answer: **B**

pp. 58–59 Humphrey's Colour Wordsnake

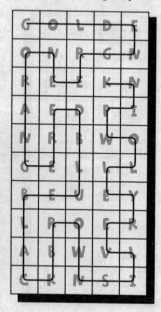

pp. 62–63 Humphrey's Haikus
1. Dog 2. Frog 3. Hamster

pp. 64–65 Aldo's Word Ladder 2
LOCK, SOCK, SICK, TICK, PICK, PACK,
PARK, DARK, DART, CART, CARE, CAGE

p. 66 Another Mysterious Message . . .
Answer: **SNOW**

pp. 68-69 **Boat Bonanza**

Answer: **D**

p. 70 **Boat Wordsearch**

L	O	N	G	B	O	A	T	F	O
N	A	C	S	E	Y	G	P	E	T
E	J	U	N	K	A	J	N	R	A
R	C	B	Y	M	T	I	J	R	P
A	S	T	C	I	R	B	E	Y	T
K	N	A	H	A	H	O	R	Y	O
O	I	O	M	K	N	S	J	A	B
G	R	B	T	M	Y	O	G	C	I
Y	U	R	S	A	E	K	E	H	M
S	H	I	P	C	K	O	J	T	N

pp. 72-73 **Pirate Puzzle**

1 PARROT
2 GOLD
3 MAP
4 ISLAND
5 SKULL

T	O	R	R	A	P	L	E	U
I	M	U	T	O	L	R	N	P
U	H	M	O	I	U	R	M	S
P	A	D	H	S	H	O	O	K
N	I	T	A	L	S	K	I	U
D	K	E	O	A	S	A	I	L
S	R	O	L	N	M	U	T	L
T	H	R	U	D	P	N	I	R
P	I	H	S	I	K	K	A	H

pp. 76–77

Humphrey's Pirate Secret Code

Message reads:

AHOY THERE ME HEARTIES!

p. 79 Help Humphrey get Home

Humphrey picks up five Nutri-nibbles along the way.

pp. 80–83 **How much do you know about Humphrey?**

Answers: 1. Read and write

2. A teacher

3. Mr Morales

4. Giggling

5. A ghost

6. A dog

7. Room 26

8. A tall ship

9. Humphrey gets out of his cage

10. Boing!

11. A lake

12. Wacky Wednesday